The Kitchen God

Adeline Foo

Illustrations by

Lee Kowling

The Kitchen God

Text © Adeline Foo 2008
Illustrations © Lee Kowling 2008

First published in Singapore in 2008 by

BOOKSMITH *productions*
booksmit@singnet.com.sg

With the support of

National Heritage Board, Singapore

Distributed by
MarketAsia (S) Pte Ltd
601 Sims Drive #04–05, Pan-I Complex
Singapore 387382
Telephone: (65) 6744 8483 / (65) 6744 8486, Fax: (65) 6744 8497
Website: www.marketasia.com.sg
E-mail: marketasia@pacific.net.sg

Printed in Singapore

ISBN-13: 978-981-08-0805-1

National Library Board Singapore Cataloguing in Publication Data

Foo, Adeline, 1971-.
The Kitchen God / Adeline Foo; illustrations by Lee Kowling. – Singapore : Booksmith Productions, 2008.
p. cm.
ISBN-13 : 978-981-08-0805-1

1. Singaporean fiction (English). 2. Children's stories, Singaporean (English) I. Lee, Kowling. II. Title.

PR9570.S52
S823   OCN 228115186

In memory of my

grandmother,

Puteh

– Adeline

For

Kai

– Kowling

*The author wishes to thank the National Heritage
Board and Asian Civilisations Museum for advice,
support and loan of pictures under "Peranakan Facts".*

*Thanks also to Peter Lee from the Peranakan
Association, for his invaluable editorial advice.*

Glossary of Peranakan terms used

amah	servant
batu lesong	mortar and pestle
gerago	tiny dried shrimp
kueh kueh	cakes
Mama	grandmother

"Perut rumah" or the stomach of the kitchen. That was what Puteh called it, her grandmother's beloved kitchen. It provided a hive for the family's life and activities. Here, Mama would oversee all cooking chores and the offering of food to pray to deities and ancestors. It was also Puteh's "playground".

Puteh loved accompanying Mama in the kitchen. She enjoyed being given little tasks like peeling potatoes or pounding spices in the batu lesong.

At times when Mama wasn't looking, Puteh would make her own face powder. She would soak rice grains in water, then dry and pound them till they are fine.

She would store this special powder in a glass jar. In the night, she would wet the powder to form a paste, then coat her face and arms.

And, if she remembered to steal some cucumber slices, she would make a face mask and pretend to be a ghost!

There was another spot in the kitchen where Puteh loved. It was the backyard, where she loved watching her amah pound gerago into a paste, which was then salted, dried and stored.

This was Mama's belachan. She ate it toasted and pounded with chillies. She would have this with rice, for every meal.

One morning, Puteh decided she would try cooking rice for Mama. Amah wasn't in the kitchen. "How difficult can it be?" she wondered.

Filling a pot to the brim with water, Puteh threw in a fistful of rice grains in it. She recalled how Amah lighted the stove with matches, and she did the same with her "stove".

After a few tries, she got the fire going.

Feeling excited, Puteh stood back to watch her rice cook. After a while, she got worried. The fire got hotter and she felt nervous. No one was around in the kitchen. She regretted cooking the pot of rice.

The pot of water started boiling and water overflowed. Puteh screamed when water hit the fire and caused it to leap upwards! She was frightened as she saw the fire burning out of control.

Amah rushed into the kitchen just at that
moment. She removed the pot from the fire and
doused the flames with water.

Puteh looked at the mess and started sobbing. "I'm so sorry, please don't tell Mama," she pleaded.

Feeling sorry for causing the mess, Puteh helped Amah with cleaning the kitchen.

A few weeks later, it was spring-cleaning time before the Lunar New Year! Puteh loved this time of the year best. She would help Mama with baking all the kueh kueh.

That afternoon, Puteh saw Amah setting out a small feast of fruits with some kueh at the altar of Datok Dapoh, the Kitchen God.

"What are you doing?" Puteh asked.

"Mama is praying to the Kitchen God. He is going back to Heaven to report to Ting Kong," Amah said.

"What is he reporting?" Puteh asked suspiciously.

"About what we have been doing in the house," Amah said, giving her a wink.

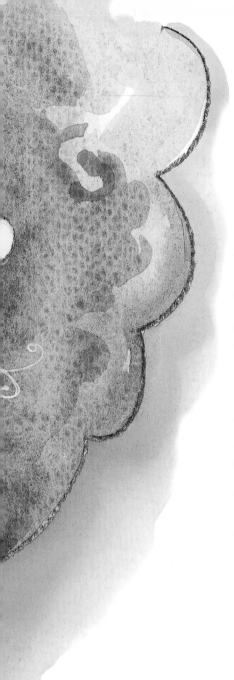

Puteh was feeling worried. She was afraid that the Jade Emperor was going to punish her for the fire she started in the kitchen.

She looked on as Amah set out the candles and urn in front of the altar. Finished with her preparation, Amah left the kitchen to fetch Mama to do the prayers.

Puteh had to act fast. Looking around the kitchen, she decided that she had to "silence" the Kitchen God. She took the lid off from the wok Mama had set to steam her kueh bakol, or nian gao, as her amah called it. It was Puteh's favourite kueh, a sweet brown glutinous rice cake.

The kueh hadn't set yet. It was still soft. Picking up a ladle, Puteh scooped out some of the sticky paste. She ran to the altar of the Kitchen God with the ladle.

For a moment, she hesitated. Then she smeared his mouth with it. "Eat this and please don't say anything bad about me," she pleaded.

Puteh then ran to put the lid back on the wok. She sneaked out of the kitchen and ran to hide in her room.

Before long, she heard Mama shrieking from downstairs. She came out of her room to see what was happening.

Mama was scolding Amah, "Did you take off the cover too soon? My kueh bakol is now spoilt. The steam is not hot enough!" she grumbled.

28

29

Five minutes later, Mama screamed again. "What happened to my Datok Dapor? His face is so dirty!"

31

Puteh watched anxiously as she saw the
Kitchen God being taken aside to be cleaned.

In the night when everyone was asleep, Puteh sneaked back into the kitchen. She brought out her face powder and mixed it with water.

She used the paste to smoothen the Kitchen God's mouth gently. Then she took out Mama's kueh bakol and offered it as an apology. "I'm really sorry, please don't punish me!"

Puteh slept better that night, knowing that the Kitchen God had been appeased.

Peranakan Facts

Traditionally, Peranakans practised Chinese religion – a diverse mix of folk beliefs, ancestor worship, Confucianism, Taoism and Buddhism which their forefathers brought with them from Southern China. As the community evolved, the Peranakans also adopted beliefs borrowed from other local communities in Malacca, and later Singapore and Penang. They also evolved their own traditions and customs, which were distinct from the religion as it was practised in China. The worship of Ting Kong, the Jade Emperor in Heaven, and the Kitchen God were two examples of religious practices the Peranakans observed.

Through the colonial period, the Peranakans largely maintained their traditional religious practices. However, a shift began in the late nineteenth century and continued after the Second World War. As times were difficult, some Peranakans simplified or even stopped practising traditional rites and ceremonies because of the substantial expenses and great effort required. Over time, some Peranakans became Christians while many others turned to more authentic interpretations of Buddhism or Taoism, thus abandoning the strict rituals of traditional Peranakan religious practices.

Peranakan Food

Peranakan food is well known in the mainstream culture of Singapore and Malaysia. It is a fusion of different influences, mainly Chinese cuisine that has been modified with Malay, Indian, Thai, Indonesian and European influences. Many Peranakan women of the past were skilled cooks who would train their daughters to cook just as well, with family recipes passed down through the generations.

One well known Peranakan food heritage item is the *sambal belachan*, a pounded condiment of chillies and fermented prawn paste mixed with lime juice. A Peranakan family would have this at almost every meal.

Mortar (Batu Lesong)
Straits Settlements c. 1900
Granite
Used for crushing and pounding ingredients, for example, in making sambal belachan
The Peranakan Museum

Mill (Batu Bo)
Straits Settlements c. 1900
Granite
Gift of Mr Ang Yang Buay
Used for grinding flour from rice, for example, in making kueh bakol
The Peranakan Museum

The Importance of Rice

Rice, a staple of Asian diet, has other significance in Peranakan culture. In the offerings of *kueh* or cakes to ancestors and deities, there are four main types – wet or dry, or made of rice or glutinous rice. One mandatory item used in Peranakan worship is the *kueh bakol*, or *nian gao* as the Chinese call it. It is usually prepared days before the Lunar New Year.

The glutinous nature of *kueh bakol*, representing sticking through thick and thin, symbolises family unity. Made from grounded glutinous rice flour and sugar, it is steamed in a mould fashioned like a basket lined with banana leaves. It has a distinctive golden caramel colour.

One other significant use of rice is in making *bedak sejok* (cool powder) to achieve the smooth porcelain complexion of a *nonya*. A "talcum" cum "mask" originally created in the kitchen of the *nonya*.

The Kitchen God

The Kitchen God is the protector of the hearth. He is a family deity who is reputed to be the inventor of fire. It is said that he would make an annual visit to Heaven, presided by the Jade Emperor, to report on the household he had been looking after. Representations of the god range from a simple piece of plain red paper to fanciful paintings. Offerings to the Kitchen God, made a week before the Lunar New Year, usually comprise sweet dishes, as the intention is to sweeten him up so that he would make a favourable report on the family.

Cosmetic Box
A miniature porcelain container for use as a cosmetic box, limited and confined largely to a face powder called bedak sejok.
Early Republican period (1911–1930), China
The Peranakan Museum

Kitchen God Altar
Malacca 2007
Courtesy of Asian Civilisations Museum